Reader's Passages to Accompany

THE CRITICAL READING INVENTORY

Assessing Students' Reading and Thinking

Mary DeKonty Applegate
St. Joseph's University

Kathleen Benson Quinn
Holy Family University

Anthony J. Applegate
Holy Family University

PEARSON

Merrill
Prentice Hall

Upper Saddle River, New Jersey
Columbus, Ohio

LAP
AP56r
2004

Vice President and Executive Publisher: Jeffery W. Johnston
Senior Editor: Linda Ashe Montgomery
Editorial Assistant: Laura J. Weaver
Production Editor: Linda Hillis Bayma
Production Coordination: Emily Hatteberg, Carlisle Publishers Services
Design Coordinator: Diane C. Lorenzo
Cover Designer: Jim Hunter
Cover image: Corbis
Production Manager: Pamela D. Bennett
Director of Marketing: Ann Castel Davis
Marketing Manager: Darcy Betts Prybella
Marketing Coordinator: Tyra Poole

This book was set in Galliard by Carlisle Communications, Ltd. It was printed and bound by Courier Kendallville, Inc. The cover was printed by Phoenix Color Corp.

Photo Credits: Kathleen Quinn, pp. 38, 39, 40, 41, 43, 44; Thomas Jenkins, Jr., pp. 46, 47.

Pearson Education Ltd.
Pearson Education Singapore Pte. Ltd.
Pearson Education Canada, Ltd.
Pearson Education—Japan

Pearson Education Australia Pty. Limited
Pearson Education North Asia Ltd.
Pearson Educación de Mexico, S.A. de C.V.
Pearson Education Malaysia Pte. Ltd.

10 9 8 7 6 5 4 3 2 1
ISBN: 0-13-048621-3

Contents

Word Lists

Word Lists

1. the	1. of
2. a	2. have
3. was	3. big
4. he	4. day
5. go	5. came
6. boy	6. house
7. stop	7. play
8. come	8. little
9. and	9. saw
10. her	10. thing
11. to	11. fly
12. like	12. jump
13. am	13. went
14. get	14. take
15. not	15. give
16. can	16. off
17. see	17. could
18. will	18. many
19. me	19. want
20. you	20. out

Word Lists

1. family	1. teacher
2. hear	2. clean
3. school	3. remember
4. happy	4. horse
5. feet	5. anyone
6. together	6. birthday
7. fish	7. garden
8. pet	8. street
9. blue	9. guess
10. before	10. pretty
11. children	11. always
12. where	12. walking
13. farm	13. pull
14. surprise	14. fast
15. friend	15. have
16. drop	16. spring
17. will	17. when
18. made	18. help
19. bike	19. know
20. game	20. brother

Word Lists

1. enter	1. doesn't
2. change	2. concern
3. lesson	3. sample
4. think	4. official
5. music	5. given
6. trust	6. present
7. human	7. decorate
8. pencil	8. windshield
9. mail	9. exercise
10. phone	10. finish
11. fright	11. enjoyable
12. unusual	12. wrong
13. they'll	13. daughter
14. bread	14. quiet
15. forest	15. morning
16. early	16. huge
17. hurt	17. covered
18. water	18. thought
19. because	19. creature
20. hour	20. people

Word Lists

1. bravely	1. athletic
2. embarrass	2. psychology
3. important	3. realize
4. guarantee	4. ridiculous
5. magical	5. successful
6. prevent	6. reluctant
7. typical	7. consideration
8. vision	8. mountain
9. handle	9. partial
10. ledge	10. graceful
11. wounded	11. applause
12. defend	12. survival
13. jungle	13. materials
14. seasonal	14. pressure
15. different	15. license
16. through	16. vehicle
17. interesting	17. definite
18. necessary	18. experience
19. medicine	19. predictable
20. mysterious	20. conform

Word Lists

1. continuous	1. acquiesce
2. uncertainty	2. discrepancy
3. imperative	3. figurative
4. precious	4. connotation
5. appreciation	5. reiterate
6. regularity	6. vehement
7. disregard	7. subsidiary
8. encyclopedia	8. innocuous
9. computerized	9. mandatory
10. prognosis	10. tangential
11. synthesize	11. fathomable
12. journalist	12. cursory
13. opportunity	13. impervious
14. participated	14. poignant
15. employment	15. exuberant
16. nucleotide	16. ambidextrous
17. occurrence	17. suave
18. holocaust	18. officious
19. obsolete	19. ultimatum
20. irony	20. limpid

Narrative Passages: Form A

(pp. 11–44)

At the Library

"I want a book.
I want a good book.
Please find a pet book for me."

"Here is a cat book.
I can read you this cat book," said Mom.
"No, I do not like that book."

"Here is a dog book.
I can read you this dog book," said Mom.
"No, I do not like that book."

"What pet would you like to have?" asked Mom.
"I would like to have a bird."
"That's a good pet," said Mom.
"Here is a bird book."

"Oh, I like that book.
Please read me that book!"

The Baker

"Come in!" said the baker.
"I like to bake!
Look at the big cakes!
Look at the little cakes!"

"I want a big cake," said Jane.
"The cake is for my birthday party.
Four girls will come.
I will be four years old."

"I want a big cake," said Bill.
"The cake is for my birthday party.
Seven boys will come.
I will be seven years old."

"I want a big cake," said Mom.
"The cake is for my little girl.
She will be two years old.
We will have a party."

"I want the cake now," cried the little girl.
"I don't want a party."

"Look," said the baker.
"Here is a cupcake for you."

"Thank you!" said Mom.

The Little Fish

"Come Blue! Come Red!" said Mother Fish.

"Come, let's eat dinner."

Blue went to eat dinner.

Red saw a big fish come by and she chased the big fish away.

"Go away! This is our home!" said Red.

"What great food!" said Blue.

"Yes, this is good food," said Mother Fish. "Come and eat, Red."

But Red would not eat because she did not want to let the big fish come close.

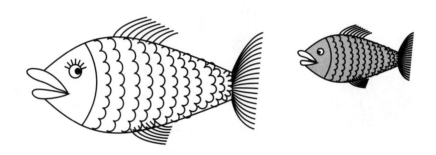

"Come Blue! Come Red!" said Mother Fish.

"Come, let's look at our pretty world."

Blue looked and looked.

Red saw a little fish come by and she chased the little fish away.

"Go away! This is our home!" said Red.

"Come and look, Red," said Mother.

But Red would not look because she did not want to let the little fish come close.

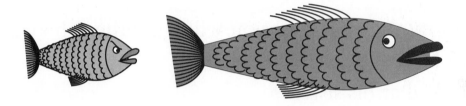

"Come Blue! Come Red!" said Mother Fish.
"We will have work to do tomorrow and we need to
   sleep."
Mother Fish fell asleep right away.
Blue fell asleep right away.
But Red could not sleep because she was still angry.

Learning to Fish

Pat said, "This is not fun!"

He was learning how to fish with his sister.

But the fish would not bite.

Pat jumped up. He shook the fishing rod.

He tried to get his bait closer to the fish.

"Don't move the rod or you will scare the fish away,"
   said Dad.

Pat looked at his sister.

She had caught three fish already.

Then Pat threw some stones into the water.

"You will scare the fish away," said Dad.

Pat was angry. He moved his rod and tried to make a
   fish take his bait.

This time Dad just watched.

Pat dropped his rod on the dock and walked away
   angry.

He sat on the shore and would not talk to his father or
   sister.

Just then a big fish took his bait.

Dad called, "Come quick! You've caught a fish!"

But Pat was not fast enough.

The fish pulled the whole rod into the deep water.

Where Is the Dog?

Jan waited at the door. She was waiting for the car to come. Aunt Saru was coming for a visit and she was bringing Sally. Jan loved to play with Sally and she loved Aunt Saru, too.

"Here they are!" Jan called to Mother. Jan ran outside to meet Sally and Aunt Saru.

"Look what I have," said Sally. Sally showed Jan her little white puppy.

"Can I hold the puppy?" asked Jan.

"Oh, yes," said Sally.

Sally took the puppy into the house.

Jan and Sally played with the puppy. Then they read books and played games. They had fun.

Then Sally went to help her mother. Jan played with the puppy. After lunch, Sally looked for her puppy. She looked and looked but she could not find her.

Aunt Saru and Mother helped her look. They asked Jan to help find the puppy.

"She is outside," said Jan.

"How did she get out?" asked Mother.

"She wanted to go out," said Jan.

"So I let her go."

Aunt Saru and Mother ran outside. Everyone looked and looked for the puppy. Jan was afraid.

Then Sally saw the puppy sitting under a car.

Everyone was happy!

"You can not let the dog go out," said Aunt Saru.

"She is too young. She will get lost."

The Pigs Get a Job

Father Pig had a big apple farm.

He had two sons.

Their names were Pete and Jake.

They worked every day with Father.

Soon Pete and Jake got older.

They were ready to leave home.

Pete bought an apple farm.

He remembered working very hard with Father.

"I will find someone to work hard for me," he said.

He asked a little pig to work for him.

The little pig worked hard.

But Pete wanted more money.

He told the little pig to work harder.

The little pig came to work early.

He picked more apples.

But he was always tired.

He did not like his job.

Jake bought an apple farm too.

He remembered the fun he had working with Father.

"I will find someone to work with me," he said.

He asked a little pig to work with him.

Jake and the little pig worked together every day.

Jake said, "You can keep all the extra apples we pick."

The little pig came in early.

He worked longer every day.

But he was happy.

He sold his apples.

He made more money.

Soon Jake had to find more pigs to work with him.

The Race

Spencer was the fastest animal in the jungle. All of the other animals knew it. Spencer made sure of that. He would say, "No one can beat me! You are all too afraid to race!" It was true. No one wanted to race against Spencer. He always won. Then he would brag even more.

One day another family of cats moved in. Spencer ran up to the new family. He said, "I'm the fastest animal in the jungle. Do you want to race?" The father said, "No, thank you. But maybe our daughter Annie will race with you." Annie smiled and said, "Yes. I'd love to race." Soon the two cats were running for the finish line. Spencer was winning as always. But Annie was very fast. She raced past him and crossed the finish line first.

The other animals cheered in surprise. But Spencer cried, "I want another chance!" They raced again and again. But the result was still the same. There was a new champion in the jungle and her name was Annie.

All the animals came over to talk to Annie. But Spencer went away angry. Annie was a little sad. She hoped that Spencer would be her friend. "Well, at least we won't have to listen to him brag again," said the fox. The next day Spencer was back. The first thing he said was, "I can jump higher than anybody in the jungle! No one can beat me!" The other animals groaned and rolled their eyes. Nothing had changed after all.

The Roller Coaster Ride

Today it was finally Jessie's birthday. She jumped out of bed and called to her mom. "Mom, can you come here and see how tall I am?" She ran to the wall and waited. Mother marked the spot where Jessie had grown since her last birthday. "I made it!" shouted Jessie. "I'm tall enough to ride the roller coaster now!" On Saturday, Jessie, her mom, and Aunt Jane would go to the park. Then she could take her first ride!

Mom was too afraid to ride so Aunt Jane took Jessie to the line to wait their turn. Jessie and Aunt Jane jumped into a car and pulled the bar over their heads. Then they waited for the ride to start. "Let's get going," thought Jessie. Soon the ride started and Jessie was really excited. She felt very grown up. Then the car climbed higher and higher. It came down and went faster and faster. Jessie was so afraid that she thought she was going to die.

Jessie held Aunt Jane's arm. She covered her face and screamed. Jessie prayed that the ride would end. "Don't let me die," she prayed, "and I'll never ride a roller coaster again." Aunt Jane hugged Jessie. Jessie opened her eyes and she saw people laughing and screaming. Aunt Jane was laughing too. They were all having fun.

The car slowed and then stopped. The ride was finally over. "Aunt Jane," said Jessie, "Can we do it again?"

The Farm Vacation

It was five o'clock in the morning when David heard his grandfather call. David never got up this early before but he didn't mind at all! He was visiting his grandfather's farm for the first time and he was excited. He had always wanted to be a farmer and now he would have his chance. Besides, Grandpa had horses too and David looked forward to learning how to ride.

When David ran into the kitchen, Grandfather said, "Eat a good breakfast, Dave. We've got a lot to do this morning. We'll start with the hay."

"Don't rush him!" said Grandma. "Are you sure you want to work with Grandpa all day?" she asked David.

"Sure am!" said David. He gulped down his breakfast and dashed out to help load the hay wagon. He never knew hay was so heavy.

"You finish up here while I get the tractor. We've got some work to do in the garden," said Grandpa.

David walked over to the garden and climbed on to the tractor. Up and down they drove, row after row, turning up the soil as they went. "Lunch time," said Grandpa when the sun was overhead.

"When do the horses get fed?" David asked Grandma as he walked into the kitchen.

"Do you want to do that after lunch? You've worked so much already," said Grandma.

"Don't forget, honey," said Grandpa, "We've got lots to do. That's how life is on the farm."

"That's OK," said David. "Maybe I better stay and help Grandpa."

After lunch, David worked under the hot sun, helping Grandpa dig postholes for a new fence. Then David and Grandpa picked corn and brought it to their roadside stand. David was trudging slowly back toward the house when Grandma called, "Do you want to feed the horses?"

David ran to the barn and helped to feed the horses. "I wish I could ride you," he said to each one as he rubbed its nose. "Maybe Grandpa will teach me!" David fell asleep immediately that night but when the sun rose the next morning, he was not so eager to get up. He had the feeling that today would be another day just like yesterday. As it turned out, he was right.

"Do you still want to be a farmer?" asked Grandfather at the end of the week. "I'm not so sure," David replied. "If the sun rose at ten o'clock and there wasn't so much hard work, then maybe farming would be more fun."

The Championship Game

At the end of a long softball season, Jill's team made it to the championship game. They would play against the top team in the league, the Ramblers. Before the game, the teams had batting and fielding practice. Jill watched her teammates. She knew that they would have a hard time winning. Their shortstop kept dropping the ball during fielding practice. Their starting pitcher was as wild as she had ever been. Jill thought that if her team was going to win, she would have to be the one to step forward. Soon the coach called the players in to sing the national anthem. Jill thought to herself, "This is just like it will be when I get to the pros." She knew the other players were nervous but not her! She couldn't wait to start the game.

Early in the game, Jill's team took a 1–0 lead. Jill came up to bat with a runner on second. But the umpire called her out on strikes. She couldn't believe that he called such a terrible pitch a strike! She really wanted to say to him, "You just called out Jill, the best player on the team." By the third inning, the lead was 3–0. Things were looking good for the team. But Jill still didn't have a hit. Her next time up, she hit a long fly to left. When the ball was caught, she blamed a gust of wind for taking away her home run.

Then the Ramblers scored four runs in their half of the inning. Now Jill had her chance to be the star. There were runners on second and third. With two strikes she got the pitch she was looking for. She swung with all her might. She couldn't believe that she missed it. Jill sat down, angry that the sun had gotten in her eyes at the wrong time. She just couldn't see the ball. Then the shortstop lined a double to left field and scored the two runs that the team needed. The pitcher struck out their last batter and Jill's team won 5–4. The team went wild, but Jill didn't feel like celebrating. Even after the team picture, Jill felt terrible. It was her worst game all season and it was the biggest game of the season, too. She wished that she had done better in front of all those people.

The Vacation

Juan burst into his sister's room. "Only eight more days!" he shouted.

"I started packing already!" said Maria. "I can't wait to see what Florida is like."

Juan and Maria had started every day for the last two weeks talking about their Florida vacation. Mom and Dad were just as eager as they were.

But that evening, Father walked into the house, looking like a ghost. "What's wrong?" Mother asked. "No more overtime for the rest of the year," he stammered. Mother knew that they were going to use the overtime money to pay for the hotel rooms and the plane tickets to Florida. This was their first family vacation!

Mr. Ruiz struggled as he told the children that they would have to cancel their vacation. Juan ran up to his room crying while Maria hugged her father and sobbed.

"Let me see what I can do," said Mrs. Ruiz as she left the room.

She was smiling from ear to ear when she returned. "I just spoke with my brother Sal and he said that we could use his van to drive to Florida and we can stay with his wife's sister!"

Maria was excited with the news but Juan was angry! That wasn't the fun vacation he had been dreaming of for weeks. He had never flown on an airplane and he had never stayed in a hotel.

During the trip, the family stopped to look at different sights along the way. But every time, Juan refused to leave the van. He was irritated with their jabbering about what they had seen at each stop. The following day, Juan again sat in the van while the others went out to see a nearby river. Suddenly, Maria came rushing back to the van. "Juan! Juan!" she called, "Hurry, there's an alligator!" Juan jumped out of the van and dashed the quarter mile to where his parents were standing.

"You missed it," said his father sadly. "It's gone!"

Maria, Mom, and Dad told Juan how they first saw the alligator sunning itself on the bank of the river. Maria had quietly run back to get Juan but a squawking bird startled the alligator and it dashed into the river. Everyone saw how disgusted Juan was and no one said a word for over twenty minutes.

"You know, Juan . . . ," began Mother.

"I know, Mom," said Juan. "I've been missing one of the best chances I've ever had! But I won't do it again!"

Autumn Leaves

"Libby, come here quick," I called. "The leaves are all falling." It is fall and my little sister, Libby, and I will have to rake the leaves together every day. Mom said that Libby is finally old enough to help with the chores and that I have the job of showing her how to clean up the yard. If we don't rake up the leaves, they will clutter up the lawn, the sidewalks, and even the rainspouts. Mom says that falling leaves are messy and dangerous, especially when they are wet.

"Look at all the leaves, Sue!" shouted Libby. "I want to go out and play right now!" I told her that we couldn't play just then. "Mom wants us to rake the leaves up. If it rains, people walking by our house might slip and fall."

"Please, Sue. Let's just jump in them for a little while," she begged. So I told her that if she would help me clean up afterwards, we could pile them up into a big mound and jump in. She was so excited that she promised to help me.

We went out and raked the leaves into a big pile and then we shouted, "One, two, three, jump!" And we jumped on the pile of leaves again and again until the leaves were scattered over the entire yard. Then I told Libby that it was time to rake them up, but Libby just wanted to keep playing. While she played, I had to gather the leaves and put them in the trash bags myself. Then I had to drag all of the bags out to the sidewalk for the trucks to come and pick up the next morning. I knew that more leaves would fall tomorrow but I wondered if Libby would help me clean them up then.

The next day, I had piano lessons so I didn't get home until late. I was surprised to find that Libby had gone outside and raked the leaves herself. But then she remembered the fun she had the day before and she jumped in them and they flew all over the yard. When I saw the mess I told Libby that she would have to clean up the leaves. I even offered to help her rake them up before Mom came home. But Libby ran away to play with her friend and I was left to do all of the work again. I really wanted to just leave everything there in the yard but I knew that Mom would be disappointed. Falling leaves can be fun for kids but grown-ups don't see it that way. I think I'm starting to see the reason.

Getting What You Want

Many years ago a young woman named Winnie Yua lived in a small Chinese village where her family kept a few rice paddies. Winnie's family was very poor. Winnie was the oldest of five girls and she would help her father take the rice to the city and sell it on market days. Her parents had always hoped for a son who would be able to go to school and perhaps work in the city for better pay. They never had their son but their daughters were all good and kind and worked hard on the farm with their parents.

One day in the marketplace, Winnie heard news from the province that the emperor had announced a counting contest. The winner would get a valuable, secret prize but only boys were permitted to participate.

"Father, I wish I were a boy. I know that I can count very well. It isn't fair that only boys can join."

"Winnie, you really need to stop wishing you were a boy. Sometimes I think it is our fault that you feel that way. You are a good daughter and a great help to us. I know it isn't fair that the emperor is allowing only boys to participate but that is the way it is. Perhaps one day things will change but you must accept your fate for now."

Winnie honored and respected her father, but she still wanted a chance to win a valuable prize and help her family. Helping at the market had made her an excellent counter. She could calculate bills and change without an abacus. And she never made a mistake. So on the day of the competition, Winnie disguised herself as a young man and entered the contest. One by one the others failed but Winnie knew her numbers well. At the end of the contest, she was the only one left. She had achieved her goal!

Now the emperor's minister came forward to award the prize. Winnie's heart was pounding. It seemed as if everyone in the entire city was there to hear the announcement. She prayed that no one would recognize her. All she wanted was to take the money, go home to her own village, and surprise her family, especially her father. Then the minister spoke in a loud voice, "The emperor has decreed that the winner of this contest is the man who will marry his only daughter!"

The Player

Rasheed was excited to be playing on his first basketball team. He hadn't played much basketball but he had always been big and fast and a good athlete. But this time things were different. The first time he had the ball, Rasheed dribbled it off his foot and out of bounds. The next two times, a quicker player stole it away from him. Finally Rasheed had his first chance to shoot the ball but he missed everything, even the backboard. Soon his teammates stopped passing the ball to him, even when he was open under the basket. His team lost the game badly and Rasheed went home angry with his team and angry with basketball.

That night, Rasheed went to his father and told him that he wanted to quit the basketball team. "I'm no good at basketball and the team is no good either," he said.

"Well, if you want to quit, that's your decision," said Mr. Singer. "But I think if you really want to, you can become a whole lot better and so can your team. Maybe you shouldn't just do things that are easy for you." Rasheed had to think this one over. Rasheed knew that whenever his father said, "It's your decision, but . . . " he really meant that he'd like Rasheed to think it over very carefully. Down deep, he knew that his father would be disappointed if he never even tried to become a better player.

Rasheed knew that his father wouldn't be much help at teaching him basketball but he had heard stories about their new neighbor, Mr. Armstrong, being named to the all-state team in high school. When Rasheed asked Mr. Armstrong if he could teach him basketball, Mr. Armstrong's eyes lit up. He said, "You stick with me, kid, and you'll be the best basketball player ever!" Rasheed laughed as the two of them took turns shooting baskets in Mr. Armstrong's back yard. But soon Rasheed was sweating and breathing hard as his new teacher put him through one basketball drill after another. Finally, Mr. Armstrong said, "Time to call it a day! But be here same time tomorrow and we'll do it again." Rasheed worked hard and even after just a few days, he could feel himself becoming more confident in his ability. When it was time for the next game, Rasheed scored eight points, grabbed five rebounds, and didn't lose the ball once. His team still lost the game but his teammates couldn't believe how much better he had become.

After the game, Mr. Singer put his arm around his son and said, "I'm really proud of the decision you made, Rasheed. You worked awfully hard and it really showed."

"Thanks, Dad. Thanks for not letting me quit the team."

"Who told you that you couldn't quit? It wasn't me!" Rasheed just smiled.

The Motor Bike

Vic sprinted down the street knowing that Jameer would be waiting for him. For the past several months they had been meeting with Mr. Hunter before school started to discuss the books they were reading. On the way, Vic's mind wandered back to his third grade teacher, Ms. Woodson, and how she had changed his way of thinking. She helped him see that reading and learning could help people improve their lives.

"Guess what?" hollered Jameer when Vic was still a distance away. "I'm getting that incredible motor for my bike that I've been telling you about. Everybody in the family gets something special for their sixteenth birthday and this is my special gift!" Vic was happy for his old friend but he couldn't help feeling just a little envious too. He really wished that he had something exceptional to look forward to on his birthday.

Mr. Hunter started class and the book discussion turned toward the influences and contributions of parents to the lives of authors. Vic realized with a growing sense of discomfort that he had absolutely nothing to add to the conversation. How could he tell them that he hardly ever saw his mother, that she had two jobs, and that he was the one who had to supervise his brothers and sisters? By the end of the class, his self-pity was overflowing. Mr. Hunter walked out with Vic at the end of class and said, "My wife and I would like you to spend next weekend with us. See if it's OK for you."

Vic spent the following weekend with the Hunter family. That Saturday evening, Mrs. Hunter sat with Vic after dinner and showed him photographs from her childhood. In her entire collection, she had only three photographs of her mother but when Mrs. Hunter got to the first one, her face softened. She told Vic how her mother had worked at two jobs from day to night to be sure that her children always had clothes and food. "This picture was taken shortly before she died," she said. "That was the first time I told her that I resented the fact that she had missed practically every important occasion in my life. That's when she showed me her album. She kept photos and clippings from every one of those events that she had missed because she couldn't take time off from her job. Some people can't express their love with words but they certainly can show it. We just have to have enough insight to read it."

Vic had a lot to mull over that weekend and the next day he said, "You know, Mrs. Hunter, I learned about reading from Ms. Woodson but she never taught me about the different kinds of reading; I guess we have to read things besides books. I think I'm going to try to get better at reading people. Maybe I've been getting special gifts, just like Jameer, but I never even knew it. Thanks."

The Tutor

Jack went to his room very troubled; tomorrow he had to begin participating in the school's tutoring program. As he lay in bed, all the embarrassing reading experiences from grade school bombarded his mind. He remembered having to read aloud in front of the class, stumbling over the words he couldn't pronounce. Now he had to spend one period each day in the second grade class, helping a younger student who was having problems reading. "I'll probably end up making him feel worse than I used to feel!" he thought.

"You'll really enjoy it," said Ms. Armstrong, his homeroom teacher, trying to calm Jack as he reluctantly left for his tutoring assignment the following day. "All you have to do is let your student select a book, read it to him, and then discuss it with him. Just ask him to look for different ways that the story had something to do with his life."

Jack hoped that Carl, the little boy to whom he was assigned, wouldn't notice how uncomfortable he felt reading with him. Fortunately, Carl selected a story that Jack had no difficulty reading and one that had an interesting twist, too. The story, *An Extraordinary Egg,* was about a frog who discovers a large egg, which her sister, with complete confidence, identifies as a chicken egg. When the egg hatches and an alligator emerges, the frogs continue to call it a chicken throughout the entire story. Carl laughed out loud as Jack read the story; in fact, Jack couldn't help laughing with him.

"The one frog was a real know-it-all," said Carl. "My friend Bob is just the same way because he tries to make me feel stupid. Just because he's a good reader doesn't mean that he knows everything! Do you have any know-it-all friends?"

"Quite a few," said Jack. "When they talk, they act conceited. They try to convince other people that they're great." He was impressed with Carl's insight into his friend and how he used Carl's reading difficulties as a justification to put him down.

"That's exactly what the frog in the story did too," said Carl. "She even laughed at the mother alligator for calling the creature an alligator and not a chicken. Really, somebody should have laughed at her!" Jack suddenly remembered the times that certain of his classmates had laughed at him. "Do you think laughing at people is a very good way to get them to change?" "I guess that probably wouldn't work," said Carl.

"I feel sorry for the frog who was always exploring and discovering things, but nobody at home ever got excited with her. My parents always get excited when I do anything. I think that they want me to feel smart even though I'm not a good reader. You probably never had to worry about that when you were in second grade."

"You can never really know for sure about things like that. Maybe we should talk about school experiences next time."

The Magician

Soon after the death of his father, the court magician to the Austrian king, Petruccio was named by the king to assume the post and to follow in his father's footsteps. As the magician, Petruccio would be an important figure in the king's court. He would be expected to foretell future events by reading the stars. He was also supposed to ward off evil spirits who might bring harm to the kingdom. Petruccio's father had loved his son dearly and sent him to the finest university in the world. But his study of logic and science at the university left Petruccio ill-equipped to traffic in spirits and "read" the stars. Petruccio found himself a court magician who did not believe in superstition. Petruccio's beliefs, however, mattered little to the court officials. The king needed a magician and there was no point in arguing with the king.

But Petruccio was a swift learner. He quickly realized that the best way to survive was to make the fewest predictions possible. He also developed the skill of taking credit for whatever good befell the kingdom. When the king asked him to predict future events, Petruccio would make predictions for which he had the best chance of being correct. Once the king asked Petruccio to predict whether his soon-to-be-born child would be male or female. Petruccio noted that the king had three sons and one daughter. So he correctly predicted the birth of a son. But after several years of good fortune, Petruccio's luck ran out. When the king's favorite aunt fell ill with the fever, Petruccio was asked to predict her fate. He observed that more people who had contracted the disease had died than who had survived. Thus he predicted that the aunt would die.

Petruccio was correct but he had not anticipated that the king would blame him for the death of his beloved aunt. Having resolved to behead his court magician, the king called Petruccio before him. With an ironic smile, the king asked him to foretell the manner in which he, Petruccio, would die. But the quick-thinking young man recognized the danger. He said to the king, "Your Majesty, I will die exactly three days before you." The king was dumbfounded. Instead of ordering his execution, the king ordered his guard to place Petruccio under special protection. He even commanded that they take care to be sure that Petruccio's needs were met. And so Petruccio lived for many years in comfort under the watchful care of his king.

The Friend

Alex came home from the hair salon and put on her best party dress. Tonight she would be dining at the most exclusive and expensive restaurant at the lake resort where her parents had a cabin. Her old friend Jaime, who had always liked Alex, had invited her to the dinner, but it was Jaime's visiting cousin Carlos that she was really interested in. The three of them had played tennis that afternoon and Alex couldn't wait to see the handsome and sophisticated Carlos again.

Alex had persuaded her father that she could handle the small motorboat by herself for the short trip to the restaurant dock. After all, she drove the boat more often than anyone else in the family did! Alex drove very slowly so that her hairdo would be perfect when she arrived. Soon she pulled up to the dock in her tiny boat amid all of the expensive yachts and powerboats and was glad to see that Jaime and Carlos were waiting for her. Both young men were dressed in their finest clothes but Alex had eyes only for Carlos.

Alex turned the motor off and let the boat drift closer to the dock. She stretched out with the rope to tie the boat up but nearly lost her balance. Fortunately, she was able to grab on to the end of the pier. To her horror, Alex realized that the boat was drifting further away from the dock with her feet clinging desperately to its rail. Jaime immediately jumped down to the lower dock to try to help but he was too late. Alex fell headlong into the murky water next to the dock. Alex was an excellent swimmer but swimming was the furthest thing from her mind. She didn't know how she could face all of the people who had gathered at the dock watching her. They were all very polite and sympathetic but Carlos could not hide his amusement. Jaime tried to coax Alex toward his outstretched hand, but Alex could not bear the thought of facing the growing crowd of people on the dock. For Alex the evening was ruined.

Suddenly Jaime called, "Hold on, Alex! I'm coming to save you!" She watched in disbelief as Jaime leaped into the water with a tremendous splash and surfaced next to her with a huge grin. Despite her distress, Alex couldn't help but smile and soon the two of them were hugging each other and laughing so hard that they couldn't stop. When Jaime helped Alex from the water, she didn't mind the crowd of now-smiling onlookers nearly as much as she thought she would. Jaime whispered to her, "Let's go home and change and then we'll go out and get a pizza." During the boat ride back to her house, Alex watched her old friend laugh and shiver and joke about their experience, trying very successfully to cheer her up. Alex had to admit to herself that, despite the embarrassment, she had learned a great deal that night about true friends.

Differences

Lin sat thinking in silence in the rear seat of the car as her parents drove out of the tree-lined main drive of the idyllic university campus and began the long ride home. But there was no reflection of the campus serenity in Lin's mind that morning. She was trying desperately to control her anger as she relived the events of the past few days, events that dragged her back to the days of her youth when she felt so much like an outsider. The cinema in her mind replayed the first time that Lin had met her best friends, Marilyn and Cindy. Lin was seven years old and her family had just moved into their new home when her mother called her to tell her that two girls had knocked at the front door and asked if they could play with Lin.

The three girls sat on the front porch as her new friends bombarded Lin with questions about her life in China. She had all but forgotten the feeling that came over her, like being a strange specimen captured in a bottle to be scrutinized by inquisitive students. "They don't want to be my friends," Lin blurted out to her mother late one afternoon, "they just want to show me how different I am. I don't want to play with them again." But Lin's mother simply said, "Are you talking about how they feel or how you feel?" And so Lin decided not to run away and soon she joined Marilyn and Cindy in their imaginary world in the nearby woods, reading stories of faraway lands. Within months, the girls had become inseparable and they were still the best of friends at the end of their junior year at the university. But it was the memory of being seven years old and feeling so terribly and unalterably different that consumed her during the ride home and not the friendship or the happy ending.

"You're pretty quiet, Lin," Mother said, but Lin was slow to respond. It had been her mother's idea for Lin to become acquainted with the four Chinese exchange students who began their university studies that semester. At that time Lin thought that serving as their mentor and assisting them in making the transition to American life and customs would be a marvelous way to help the girls. But their initial meeting had not been as fruitful as Lin had hoped it would be. At first, the girls sat in rapt attention and laughed as Lin shared with them stories of how she and her friends had learned to navigate the sometimes rough waters of the often convoluted campus procedures and protocol. But when Lin began to ask about their customs and point out the sharp contrasts between Chinese and American ideas of propriety and manners, the girls lapsed into an uncomfortable silence. Soon they were chattering nervously among themselves about Chinese poets and literature, books that Lin could not even read. The meeting ended awkwardly, with everyone sensing the presence of bruised egos but no one quite sure of their source.

"They seemed to relish making me feel like an outsider and you know, Mother, I can't really comprehend how a working knowledge of Chinese poetry will help them get very far in America."

"Are you certain that is what they wanted you to feel, Lin?" her mother asked. "Perhaps it was awkward for them to seem so different from you and all of the other students."

"That's no excuse for being impolite," snapped Lin, "especially when I was going out of my way to try to help them."

Later that week, on the family's long-planned trip to Niagara Falls, Lin stood mesmerized by the swiftness and intensity of the river, all very familiar but yet always somehow new. She felt her mother slip her arm around her and heard her whisper, "The river always knows where it is going, perhaps because it knows where it has been." Lin knew her mother too well to believe that this was mere idle chatter; she had learned long ago that it was worth the effort to think long and hard to uncover the sometimes arcane lesson embedded in her mother's words.

Lin woke the next morning filled with a fresh resolve for the upcoming semester at the university. She would help her new friends organize discussion groups to explore Chinese literature and culture and she knew exactly whom she could invite to participate. The groups would dedicate themselves to the celebration of diversity, differences, and friendship in the university community, for as her mother knew so well, it always helps to know where you've been.

The Injury

It seemed that the entire town was trying to fit into the Franklin High School football stadium for the final game of the season. But the buzz in the crowd was all about the recruiters from big-name colleges who had come to scout Ron, their local football and baseball hero. It seemed that their small town was finally on the map and it was a fine athlete and a fine young man who had put them there. At the end of the evening few people at the game even remembered the final score. The images that seem engraved on the minds of everyone at the game were the hard tackle, the awkward fall, and the stretcher that carried Ron to the ambulance that waited outside the field for just such emergencies. The diagnosis was grim. A torn rotator cuff would need immediate surgical repair and months of rehabilitation and there were no guarantees that Ron would ever regain the athletic skills that had set him apart from every other player in the entire league.

On his way to the hospital, Ron thought about his father, who would be anxiously praying and waiting for him there. Ron knew that his father had taken on the extra part-time job to earn the money to cover the expenses for Ron's participation in sports. His father had always been proud of his son's athletic success but Ron suspected that he was most grateful for the full scholarship it would bring, a scholarship to a private university that the family could never have afforded.

With that scholarship now in jeopardy, Ron knew that he would have to face some thorny decisions with some far-reaching consequences. But unfortunate decisions and still more regrettable consequences were things that Ron and his father had talked about for as long as Ron could remember. His father had dropped out of football because he hadn't kept up his grades. Then he had to watch his best friend, a player whom everyone recognized was not his father's equal, go on to win a football scholarship to a top-grade university and to have a thoroughly successful college career. How many times had he heard his father speculate wistfully on what might have been if he had only stayed with football? After graduation and a tour of duty in Vietnam, his father had returned determined to go on to earn a college degree, but after several months in the local community college, he became jealous of the spending money that his working friends always seemed to have. He dropped out of college and took a full-time job but he still somehow never seemed to earn enough or succeed enough to match his aspirations. Whenever he could, Ron's father would make a point of identifying the consequences he had paid and still continued to pay because of the poor decisions he had made in his youth. Ron knew that his father would be deeply disappointed in him if he made the wrong decision.

After his surgery, Ron's physical therapy was more painful than anything he had ever experienced. He began to wonder whether he really wanted to risk reinjuring the shoulder by trying to rejoin the team. But without football, what could he do to afford college? He had always been an honor roll student, but he knew that he would never qualify for an academic scholarship. Ron began to wonder whether he should drop out of sports altogether. Then he would have more time to devote to his studies. But what about the regrets that were sure to come later? What about the consequences if he made the wrong decision?

His father accompanied Ron, as always, to the doctor's office at the end of Ron's physical therapy program. The doctor told them what Ron had suspected all along: he could return to football but another injury to the shoulder could leave him with permanent damage and pain. Ron and his father drove in silence to the coffee shop where they had spent countless hours over the years discussing life's choices and consequences.

Ron wanted desperately to ask his father what he should do, but he sensed that the time for letting others decide for him had long since passed. Instead, Ron turned to his father and said, "You've never told me which regret was greater, dropping out of football or out of college."

To Ron's surprise, his father replied, "I'm really beginning to wonder if I've wasted too much of my life regretting the things that I've done. If I had stayed in college and in football, I may never have been fortunate enough to meet your mother or to have had a son like you. I may never have been nearly as contented as I've been over the years. I'm beginning to think that maybe it isn't always the choices that you make but what you make of the choices that really matters." Ron nodded; he didn't quite understand yet what his father meant but he had the distinct feeling that he soon would.

Informational Passages:
Form B

(pp. 47–73)

All Kinds of Trucks

A big, red fire truck goes fast.

It helps put out fires.

A small, green truck goes down the street.

It brings boxes to our store.

A tanker truck has a long, long hose.

It brings gas to our gas station.

A large, blue truck sprays water.

It cleans our street.

The best truck rings its bell and plays a song.

It brings me a treat.

Plants

A man needs water.
He goes to the sink.
He gets a drink of water.
A cow needs water.
She goes to the stream.
She drinks water.
A plant needs water.
It can not move.

The plant has roots.
The roots grow in the soil.
The soil has water.
The soil has food.
The roots take in the water.
The roots take in food.

People eat the plants.
The plants are good for them.
They get food from the plants.

Turtles

Turtles can be big or small.

All turtles can crawl.

Some turtles can swim.

All turtles have hard shells.

A turtle can hide in its shell and be safe.

Small turtles make good pets.

They can live near a pond or a lake.

They eat worms, bugs, and grass.

Children often catch small turtles and take them home.

They can keep them in a large cage and take care of them.

They give the turtles water and food.

Large turtles live near the sea.
They catch their food in the sea.
They stay under the water for a long time.
They can swim very fast and can live a long time.

Maps

A pilot can fly an airplane.

He takes people from state to state.

He can go a long way but it does not take a long time.

He uses a map to find his way.

A lady can drive a truck.

She drives goods from state to state.

She goes a long way too, but it will take a long time.

Sometimes she needs a map.

We can take a trip in our car.

We do not always need a map.

But sometimes we can get lost.

Then a map can help.

Maps help people find the right way.

They keep people from going the wrong way.

Black Bears

Black bears live in the U.S.

They live near woods or near mountains.

They live in dens.

The dens can be inside a tree or a cave.

They sleep all winter.

In spring, they wake up hungry.

Sometimes they can't find enough food.

They like to eat berries, honey, nuts, and acorns.

But they will eat almost anything.

If they don't find food close to home, they go out looking.

One bear and her cubs could not find enough to eat.

They came down the mountain.

They broke into someone's house.

This was very dangerous.

They took cookies, dog food, and honey.

The cubs took burgers off the grill.

People found them.

The cubs weighed only 20 pounds.

They should have weighed 50 pounds.

No wonder they were hungry.

People in Groups

Long ago people lived in groups.

They were called tribes.

They hunted and fished together.

They found plants and berries.

They moved on foot from place to place.

They followed the animals.

They killed only the animals they needed.

They did not grow their own food.

They had to work together to live.

Today people live in groups, too.

They live in cities and towns.

They still like to hunt and fish.

But now they grow their own food on farms.

They also raise their own animals.

But most people buy their food.

They have cars and planes to help them move.

But they still have to work together to live.

Army Ants

Do you ever run from ants? Some people in South America do. They run from the army ants. Army ants march in very large numbers looking for food. The ants are only about the size of your fingernail. But they have large and strong jaws. They march very slowly in a row four feet wide. But most armies are more than a mile long. All animals must get out of their way. They can bite and kill large animals and they can even kill men.

Army ants are hard to stop. They can climb over walls and trees. Not even water can stop them. They just hold onto each other with their jaws and then roll themselves into a ball. Then they can float across rivers and streams! Sometimes the ants march close to a village. Then the people must all move out. But some of the people are glad to see the ants. The ants clean up the town for them by killing small animals and pests.

The Doctor Fish

Some animals are a big help to other animals. One animal that helps others is the wrasse. The wrasse is a fish about four inches long. He is very brightly colored. He lives in the South Pacific Ocean. He is like a doctor to other fish.

His office is in the rocks called reefs. Many fish come to the doctor for help. These fish have animals that live on their bodies. They would like to have them taken off. The wrasse eats these tiny animals. He also uses his teeth to clean wounds. He helps the fish to get better.

The doctor can be very busy. Sometimes he works all day. But the doctor gets his pay too! The doctor gets the food he likes from his patients. They also protect the doctor from bigger fish. But the doctor and his patients must be careful. A fish called the blenny looks just like the wrasse. Some fish think they are coming to see the doctor. Then the blenny takes a bite out of them! That makes things worse.

The Immigrants

Between 1820 and 1920 many people moved to America. Some came to find better jobs. Others came because they were not free in their own lands. Others came because their country's leaders did not like them. Most people just came looking for a better life. They were called immigrants.

Most of these people came to America on sailing ships. Some trips took only a few weeks. Others took months. Some people could afford a cabin for themselves. They were lucky. The rest stayed in large rooms below the deck. The rooms were crowded and often dirty. The food was very poor. The ocean was sometimes rough. The trip was very dangerous.

The immigrants finally arrived in New York. Then they would wait in line for hours. They had to find out if they would be allowed to stay. There was a long line for most people. There was a short line for richer people.

Many of these new Americans were not welcome. They could not speak English. They were different and strange. They were willing to work for low wages. But some factory owners would not hire them at all. These owners all seemed to forget one thing. Almost everyone in America had family members who were immigrants themselves.

Child Slaves

Everyone knows that slavery is wrong. But slavery is still very common. And one of its worst forms is child slavery. Poor families are the most likely victims. Farm owners can make families pay for their food and shelter. The family cannot earn enough to pay the owners back. So everyone in the family works to try to pay the debt. Most of the time, they will never succeed. But the owners don't care! All those years of cheap work are too valuable.

Often the parents can no longer work. But the children must still work for the owners. The children can not go to school. They can never stop working to pay what they owe. Some owners are at least kind to the children. Then their life is a little better. But other owners are cruel. Children may not get enough food to stay healthy. If the child misses a day of work, the family must pay a fine. Then they will owe even more.

Many countries have laws against children working. But no one in the family knows about the laws. They don't know that their children have rights. And so it is very difficult to stop people from using children as slaves.

Frida Kahlo

Frida Kahlo was born in Mexico in 1907. She was an intelligent and beautiful young woman. She planned to become a doctor. But when she was 18 years old, she was hurt while riding a bus. The accident broke her back in three places. After a long time in the hospital, she had to stay in bed for months. To pass the time, Frida began to paint. She soon found her talent and her love.

Some of her friends saw that Frida's paintings were very interesting. They helped her to meet Diego Rivera, a famous Mexican painter. Diego helped Frida to develop as a painter. They soon fell in love and married. But their marriage was troubled and painful. Frida soon learned that painting helped her to deal with her feelings. She painted many pictures of herself. She often said that she was the subject she knew best of all.

Frida had many operations on her back. Her great pain and her great strength made their way into her paintings. She had a rare ability to express pain and unhappiness through art. For this reason Frida Kahlo is seen as one of the truly great talents of her time. A museum in Mexico shows only her works. She is one of very few women artists who have ever achieved that honor.

Krakatoa
(crack-uh-toe-uh)

Krakatoa was a small island volcano about five miles wide. Over many years it had grown bigger from dozens of small eruptions and lava flows. That was before the morning of August 27, 1883. At the end of that day there was almost no island left. The volcano had exploded. Almost three-quarters of the island was gone. Much of it was blown miles into the sky. The dust in the air shaded the sun for months.

It was lucky that no people lived on the island. But there were many islands close by where people did live. The huge waves caused by the blast killed many people. Some waves were as high as twelve-story buildings. They washed whole villages into the sea. Almost 36,000 people died.

The explosion of Krakatoa was heard 2,800 miles away. Windows in homes 100 miles away were broken. Many people think that the explosion was the biggest that ever happened on earth. Over the years a new volcano has risen. It is very close to the old island. Some people believe that it took Krakatoa's place. It has been named "Child of Krakatoa." Many people have read about that first great explosion. Some of them believe that we may not have heard the last of Krakatoa after all.

The Mosquito

The next time you smack a mosquito on your arm and say to yourself, "Got him!" you should think again. Actually you got *her!* Only the female mosquito does the biting. She is in search of fresh blood to feed the eggs that will soon become more little Draculas. The female mosquito finds her victims by following streams of carbon dioxide. This is the gas that is exhaled by the warm-blooded animals she seeks. The carbon dioxide guides the mosquito to her prey.

Once she has found you, she is hard to stop. Unless you hear the telltale buzzing of her wings, you will probably never know she is there. She lands very lightly on her feet. Once she has landed she inserts her long, needle-like nose into your skin. Her nose is so thin that most people never feel the needle at all. Before she can start sipping your blood, she injects a little saliva to make it thinner. Otherwise it is like trying to drink a thick milk shake through a straw. It is the saliva that the mosquito leaves behind that makes the skin itch and swell.

Some people are lucky enough to feel her and fast enough to smack her. She may leave a smear of blood on their bare arm. But they weren't fast enough. That blood they see is their own! It is no surprise that mosquitoes are not the most popular of insects, unless you happen to be a spider or a bat! In addition to being pests, they also carry and spread diseases like malaria and the West Nile virus. But until we think of a better way to control them, mosquitoes will continue to annoy any animal that has blood and thin skin.

Oil Spill

On the night of March 24, 1989, a huge oil tanker named the *Exxon Valdez* ran into a reef in Prince William Sound in Alaska. It was carrying oil from the Alaska Pipeline to the mainland United States. More than 11 million gallons of crude oil spilled from the ship. This was the largest oil spill in U.S. history. The spill was a terrible shock to the residents and Coast Guard that night. They did not know that the spill would soon get much worse.

At first, the Coast Guard tried to burn up the oil. But bad weather made controlled burning difficult. Then cleanup crews tried to scoop the oil from the water. But their equipment quickly became clogged with seaweed and thick oil. To make matters even worse, the spill site could be reached only by boat or helicopter. Crews sent to help clean oil-coated animals were slow to arrive. Then they just could not work fast enough. There were too many birds and animals that needed to be cleaned. The oil spill is estimated to have killed 250,000 sea birds, including 250 bald eagles. Nearly 3,000 sea otters and 22 killer whales were lost in the spill as well.

All in all, 140 miles of coastline were soaked with oil. Nearly 1,500 miles had some oil. Exxon Corporation has spent an estimated 2.5 billion dollars in the clean-up of the spill. The fishing industry in Alaska is still not the same. Many fishermen feel that it never will be. Experts predict that the effects of the spill will be felt for decades to come.

A Community of Wolves

Wolves are probably one of the most misunderstood animals on our planet. Many myths and legends depict wolves as tricky, cunning, and dangerous. Who doesn't remember "The Big Bad Wolf" and "Little Red Riding Hood" or the "Werewolf" legend? This image, however, couldn't be further from the truth. Wolves may be dangerous . . . to rabbits, deer, pigs, sheep, and cattle. But you don't have to worry that one will eat you or your granny up!

Actually wolves are part of a closely-knit family that consists of 2 to 10 adults and any young pups. All of the wolves in the pack share responsibility for the young. The wolves travel in packs for the sake of more successful hunting, for mutual protection, and for companionship. Wolves are also territorial. They usually travel within a specific range, sometimes up to 50 square miles.

Many experts believe that it is the wolf's eerie howl that plays on the fears of man. In fact, their howl is part of a sophisticated communication system within their group. Howling is the wolves' way of "staying in touch" over long distances. If a wolf is separated from her pack, she will begin howling. This is a cry for help as well as a call to reunite. It can, however, be very costly. If a competing pack is within her range, they may seek her out and kill her. Pups are especially vulnerable. They have not yet learned the appropriate times and places for howling.

Other purposes for howling include warning rival packs to keep moving or staking a claim on fresh-killed prey. The so-called "chorus howls" are used to make competing packs think that there are really more wolves in the pack. The next time you hear a wolf howl, you will know it is not a werewolf howling at the moon. Perhaps it is only a lost wolf looking for its pack.

Are You Afraid of Sharks?

Every summer in the United States, we hear about shark attacks. On some beaches, it is even common to see sharks swimming offshore. Other beaches will be closed because there are so many sharks swimming near the shore. But how likely is it that if you go for a dip in the ocean you will be attacked by a shark? Not very likely at all!

We are far more likely to be killed by another person than by a shark. Most scientists believe that the few shark attacks that occur are really mistakes. When we tan, the top portion of our foot turns brown while the bottom remains white. This shading is similar to that of many fish. Others think sharks mistake us for sea lions or seals, which are some of their favorite food. When they realize that they have made a mistake, most sharks simply spit out their victims and leave. Just think about it . . . if sharks wanted to have us for dinner on a regular basis, they could just come to any shore in the United States and help themselves.

Sharks should probably be more afraid of us than we are of them. The total shark population is in decline as a result of human hunting. For example, in some countries, shark fin soup is a delicacy and the fins are very much in demand. The shark fin itself is often used in ceremonial dinners. When local fishermen capture the shark, they will use the entire body, but commercial fishers have been known to follow the practice of "finning." They cut off the fins of any sharks caught in their nets. They then throw the sharks back into the sea, leaving them to bleed to death. And *we're* afraid of *them*?

Because we do not have "shark farms" as we do for catfish or shrimp, constant fishing leads to over-killing of certain kinds of sharks. They simply cannot reproduce quickly enough to keep up with the demand. Although we may fear sharks with good cause, destroying them beyond rescue may be even more harmful to us all in the long run.

Mary Jemison

Mary Jemison was born in 1743 on board a ship sailing to America. Her family settled in a rural community near what is now Gettysburg, Pennsylvania. Mary's father showed no fear of the reports of Indian raids that he heard from their neighbors. Her mother, however, had always felt differently. On April 5th, 1758, her fears came true. A party of French soldiers and Indians raided the Jemison farm. Her terrified mother told Mary to obey her captors, remember her English language, and never forget who she was. Mary was taken away by her captors. Unknown to her, Mary's parents and most of the rest of her family were killed. Mary would have to rely only on her mother's words throughout the long days of captivity.

Mary was given to a pair of Seneca Indian women whose brother had been killed in battle. The women had a simple choice. They could kill Mary in revenge for their lost brother. Or they could adopt her to replace him. They chose to adopt Mary and treated her as their own sister, with a great deal of kindness. Mary missed her parents and family and could not at first be happy. She prayed and practiced her English language every day. But she eventually came to appreciate and respect her two new sisters. At the same time, she began to recognize the qualities that the Indian tribe demonstrated in their daily life. She characterized the Indians as extremely faithful to each other, very honest and honorable in all that they did. Mary married a Seneca warrior in 1765 and had several children of her own.

After the Revolutionary War, Mary was offered her freedom by the tribe. Her son was anxious to see his mother go and live with her own people. Mary, however, could not bring herself to leave her son. She also worried about how she and her family would be treated by white people. She was afraid they might view her as a traitor. And so she chose to remain with her Indian family and spend the remainder of her days with them. Mary Jemison died in 1831, having spent more than 70 years as an Indian captive.

Old Man River

For many Midwestern Americans living along the floodplains of the Mississippi River, the Great River was the source of their livelihood. The commercial traffic that flowed daily on the river provided goods and employment for thousands of people. But as William Faulkner wrote, the river was like a mule that would work for you for ten years just for the privilege of kicking you once.

And one of the river's hardest kicks was delivered in 1993. A huge flood left 74,000 people without homes in nine states. It caused over 15 billion dollars in damage. To be sure, the Mississippi had flooded before. Old-timers in the town could remember many flood years in their lifetimes. But 1993 seemed to almost everyone to be the worst of them all. This flood broke high-water records all across the Midwest. But to the people living along the floodplains, the Great Flood of 1993 was simply another of life's challenges to be met and overcome. They would rebuild their homes with help from the Federal Emergency Management Agency (FEMA). Life would go on just as it had so many times in the past.

But this time things were different. The U.S. Congress was apparently tired of flood emergency claims year after year. Instead, they announced a grand social experiment. They would no longer help the citizens living on floodplains to rebuild their homes in the same place. Congress instructed FEMA to help them rebuild their homes and towns in locations that were not as prone to flooding. In 1993 alone, over 10,000 homes were relocated. But hardships, as always, seemed to relocate along with the homes. Many citizens complained that their new homes, built on more expensive land, drove up their mortgage debt. Others felt the loss of friends as towns and communities went their separate ways rather than relocating together.

But there were also many success stories. Many towns managed to stay intact and to plan newer and better communities. Many local leaders emerged to help their friends and fellow townspeople ease the stresses of the drastic changes in their lives. It is too early to tell whether the experiment has worked for the greater good of all. Only one thing is certain. The U.S. Congress will probably never again help flood victims to stay in the same places just to wait for the next Great Flood to strike.

The Search for Pancho Villa

America's hunt for the infamous Mexican revolutionary Pancho Villa in 1916 was in reality the result of a series of botched political, economic, and military decisions. The United States had huge business interests in Mexico, interests that were threatened by the Mexican Revolution of 1910. Anxious to protect these interests, President Woodrow Wilson decided to throw his support behind Venustiano Carranza as the Mexican president. Carranza was the man he believed to be most sympathetic to the American agenda. But Carranza was fearful of alienating his own people by showing favor to the hated neighbor to the north. He refused to give in to some of Wilson's demands. Wilson then began to supply another revolutionary, Pancho Villa, with arms and supplies. It was Wilson's hope that Villa would be more favorably inclined to the United States if he came into power.

But Villa's potential as a threat to the Mexican leader failed to materialize. Wilson decided to make his peace with Carranza and recognize his government. Villa was infuriated at the desertion of Wilson. In retaliation, he and his men killed 16 Americans traveling on a train in Mexico. But his boldest attack occurred on American soil in the town of Columbus, New Mexico, and left 19 Americans dead. Villa hoped that by provoking a counterattack by the Americans, he could turn popular opinion against Carranza and expose his ties to the United States. Then Villa would be waiting in the wings to assume the leadership of all of Mexico.

America, in its turn, launched what came to be known as the Punitive Expedition against Villa and his men. Wilson sent General John J. Pershing and 5,000 soldiers, equipped with trucks, armored vehicles, and even airplanes into Mexico to hunt down Villa and his army. But Pershing underestimated Villa's enormous support and popularity among the Mexican people. They consistently protected their local Robin Hood, giving Villa advance notice of Pershing's movements. They even supplied false information about Villa's whereabouts to Pershing's troops. After nearly two years of trying, Pershing had nothing to show for his efforts. He had not even come close to locating Villa. The Punitive Expedition was finally called off.

Despite the miserable failure of the Expedition in achieving its primary end, many historians consider it a resounding success in the larger scheme of things. With the threat of World War I looming, American troops had the chance to familiarize themselves with their new weapons and technology. In particular, their use of reconnaissance aircraft, despite its failure in the short term, led to a great deal of success in the preparation for the war against Germany.

Quasars

Ever since the dawn of humanity, searching the skies with more and more sophisticated instruments has led to a spate of new discoveries almost too breathtaking to keep up with. In the 1940s, for example, radio astronomers found that many objects in the night sky were emitting radio waves; most of these sources were common stars. But some faint blue-colored objects in the celestial landscapes were very difficult to explain. They looked like stars but they emitted a huge quantity of very intense radio and ultraviolet waves, much more than could be expected from a typical star.

It was not until 1963 that Dr. Maarten Schmidt explained the phenomenon. Examining the strange light spectrum emitted by one of the "stars," Schmidt deduced that the unusual red-shifted spectrum lines (the measure of an object's recession velocity) were part of a simple hydrogen spectrum. However, the only way that the objects could produce this type of spectrum is if they were travelling away from Earth at a speed of almost 30,000 miles per second! And if that were correct, the objects would be more than 3 billion light years away, making them the most distant and, arguably, the most fascinating objects ever discovered in our universe. Because they were not true stars, scientists dubbed the strange objects *quasars* (for quasi-stellar radio sources).

Scientists were at a loss to explain how telescopes on earth could still detect such distant objects. To be detectable from earth, quasars would have to emit light as intense as that produced by 1,000 entire galaxies but yet take up space only about the size of our own solar system. But scientists today believe that the brightness of a quasar can be accounted for by the presence of super-sized black holes in the midst of huge galaxies. Black holes suck in passing stars and clouds of gas and, in doing so, heat huge amounts of matter to such an extent that it emits stupendous amounts of light.

Because quasars are so distant, they must have been created in the very early stages of the development of the universe. Indeed, it would be logical to conclude that since it is taking 3 billion years for the light of some quasars to reach us, those quasars are no longer in existence. Only their light, still traveling over the vast expanses of the universe, is reaching us today. It is certainly true that quasars still raise more questions than scientists have answers. But quasars are objects that unquestionably challenge the imagination of scientists and laymen alike as we seek more and more answers to the mysteries of the universe.